STAYING
SAFE

Staying safe near

FIRE

Maribeth Boelts

FRANKLIN WATTS
NEW YORK • LONDON • SYDNEY

This edition first published in the UK in 1998 by
Franklin Watts
96 Leonard Street
London
EC2A 4RH

© 1997, 1998 by The Rosen Publishing Group, Inc., New York

Picture credits: p.4 © Eric Berndt/MIDWESTOCK; p.7 © David E. Spaw/MIDWESTOCK; p.8 © Scott Cook/MIDWESTOCK; p.11 © Steven Ferry; p.12 © J. Myers/H. Armstrong Roberts, Inc.; p.15 © Bob Greenspan/MIDWESTOCK; p.16 © S. Feld/H. Armstrong Roberts, Inc.; p.19 © Robert W. Slack/International Stock Photography; p.20 © J. Patton/H. Armstrong Roberts, Inc.

A CIP catalogue record for this book is available from the British Library.

ISBN 0 7496 3266 6

Printed in the United States of America

Contents

Fire

Fire is very useful. We use it for many things.
It helps us to cook our food.
It can keep us warm.
It can help us to see when it is dark.

But fire can also be very **dangerous**.
It can burn most things very quickly.
That's why it is important
to learn how to use fire safely.

◀ Fire has been used by people
for thousands of years.

Matches and lighters

Matches and **lighters** are **tools**.
Matches will light a campfire.
A lighter will light the candles on
a birthday cake.

But matches and lighters are not toys.
They can start fires!

Only grown-ups should use matches
and lighters. If you see anyone else
playing with them, tell a grown-up at once.

Matches can be dangerous▶
if they are not used in the right way.

Fire indoors

Fire is used in the kitchen to cook food.

If your home has an electric cooker,
you won't see fire. But if you have
a gas cooker, you will see blue **flames**
when the cooker is turned on.
Never to put anything in the flame.

Cooking with oil or fat can be dangerous,
because fat gets hot very quickly,
and can easily catch fire. If this happens,
call a grown-up immediately.

◄ You won't see fire on an electric stove,
but it still gets very hot.

Fire outdoors

Cooking and eating outdoors is fun
and can make a special day.
But, indoors or out, fire is always dangerous.

Doing the cooking is a grown-up's job,
but you can help by keeping well away
from the fire or barbecue.

Fireworks are another kind of fire.
Watching them is exciting, but they can also
be dangerous. Many people are hurt
by fireworks each year.

Cooking food outdoors on a barbecue is fun,
as long as everyone remembers to be careful. ▶

Every fire is dangerous

A lighted candle falling over can start a fire.
So can fat that gets too hot in a pan
on the cooker.

Fire spreads fast. In a few minutes
a whole house can be burning.

Fires can get as hot as 315°C.
Smoke from a fire is black.
It is hard to see through the smoke,
and breathing it can burn your lungs.

◀ All fires cause problems. That's why
it's important to be careful with all kinds of flame.

Smoke and fire

If you see smoke, it means there is a fire.
Smoke is dangerous. It is hot,
and can contain **poisonous** gases.
In a fire, more people are hurt
by the smoke than by the flames.

If you ever have to escape from a fire,
try to crawl on your hands and knees
under the smoke.
The air is clearer and cooler there.

It is a firefighter's job to put out a fire ▶
and make sure no one is hurt.

An escape plan

Everyone in your family should agree
a plan of escape in case there is a fire.
Think about these things:
- Are there two ways out of every room?
  You could use a window if the room
  is on the ground floor.
- Where will everyone meet outside?
- Who will ring 999, and from where?

When you have made the plan, everyone
should practise it. Practice makes perfect,
and could save your lives.

◀ Smoke detectors are another way
to protect you and your family if there is a fire.

17

Safety at night

Even at night, there are things you can do
to keep safe if there is a fire.
- If you can, sleep with your bedroom
  door shut.
- If there is a fire, roll out of bed and
  crawl under the smoke.
- Shout "Fire!" as loudly as you can.
- Crawl to the door and touch the door and
  doorhandle with the back of your hand.
  Is it hot? If it is, DON'T open it.
- Block the gap at the bottom with a blanket.
  Then crawl to another exit.

18

You can help yourself to keep safe
if there is a fire at night. ▶

Your safety is first

Now you know what to do in a fire
if the door to your room is hot.
But what if the door is cool?

Open it a crack. If there is heat and smoke
shut it at once. If there is not, look out.
If everything is clear, crawl out of the room.
Take shallow breaths so you don't choke
on any smoke and **fumes**.

NEVER go back into a room to get anything.
Your job is to get out quickly and safely.

◀ If there is a fire, you must concentrate
on getting out safely.

Getting help

If there is smoke or a fire at your home, you must **report** it at once. Ring 999 from the nearest phone. Keep calm and speak slowly. Tell the operator your name and the address of the fire. Stay on the phone until you are told to hang up.

Then go to your family's meeting place and wait for help.

Fire can be dangerous. But if you're careful and follow the rules, you'll be safe.

Glossary

Dangerous Something that is harmful.

Flame The flickering, glowing, hot part of a fire. Some flames are orangey red, others are blue. All flames are dangerous.

Fumes Gas or smoke that is harmful.

Lighter Tool used to light something with fire.

Match Short piece of wood with a tip that catches fire when scraped on a special surface.

Poisonous Something that is harmful and can cause sickness.

Report To tell someone something.

Tool Something that is used for work.

Index